MINDFIELD

MINDFIELD CREATED BY:
J.T. KRUL

MINDFIELD™ VOLUME I
ISBN: 978-1-941511-45-9 FIRST PRINTING, REGULAR EDITION 2017.
ISBN: 978-1-941511-49-7 FIRST PRINTING, COMIC BENTO VARIANT EDITION 2017.
COLLECTS MATERIAL ORIGINALLY PUBLISHED AS MINDFIELD VOLUME 1. ISSUES 0, 1-6 AND THE MINDFIELD BONUS STORIES.

PUBLISHED BY ASPEN MLT, LLC.
OFFICE OF PUBLICATION: 5701 W. SLAUSON AVE. SUITE. 120, CULVER CITY, CA 90230.
THE ASPEN MLT, LLC. LOGO® IS A REGISTERED TRADEMARK OF ASPEN MLT, LLC. MINDFIELD™ AND THE MINDFIELD LOGO ARE THE TRADEMARKS OF J.T. KRUL. THE ENTIRE CONTENTS OF THIS BOOK, ALL ARTWORK, CHARACTERS AND THEIR LIKENESSES ARE © 2017 ASPEN MLT, LLC. ALL RIGHTS RESERVED. ANY SIMILARITIES BETWEEN NAMES, CHARACTERS, PERSONS, AND/OR INSTITUTIONS IN THIS PUBLICATION WITH PERSONS LIVING OR DEAD OR INSTITUTIONS IS UNINTENDED AND IS PURELY COINCIDENTAL. WITH THE EXCEPTION OF ARTWORK USED FOR REVIEW PURPOSES, NONE OF THE CONTENTS OF THIS BOOK MAY BE REPRINTED, REPRODUCED OR TRANSMITTED BY ANY MEANS OR IN ANY FORM WITHOUT THE EXPRESS WRITTEN CONSENT OF ASPEN MLT, LLC. PRINTED IN U.S.A.

Address correspondence to:
Mindfield c/o Aspen MLT, LLC.
5701 W. Slauson Ave. Suite. 120
Culver City, CA. 90230-6946
or fanmail@aspencomics.com
Visit us on the web at:
aspencomics.com
aspenstore.com
facebook.com/aspencomics
twitter.com/aspencomics

ORIGINAL SERIES EDITORS:
VINCE HERNANDEZ AND FRANK MASTROMAURO

FOR THIS EDITION:
SUPERVISING EDITOR: FRANK MASTROMAURO
EDITORS: GABE CARRASCO
COVER AND BOOK DESIGN: MARK ROSLAN
BOOK DESIGN AND PRODUCTION: MARK ROSLAN AND GABE CARRASCO
REGULAR COVER ILLUSTRATION: ALEX KONAT, MARK ROSLAN AND JOHN STARR
COMIC BENTO VARIANT COVER ILLUSTRATION: PHIL NOTO

FOR ASPEN:
FOUNDER: MICHAEL TURNER
CO-OWNER: PETER STEIGERWALD
CO-OWNER/PRESIDENT: FRANK MASTROMAURO
VICE PRESIDENT/EDITOR IN CHIEF: VINCE HERNANDEZ
VICE PRESIDENT/DESIGN AND PRODUCTION: MARK ROSLAN
EDITOR: GABE CARRASCO
PRODUCTION ASSISTANTS: JUSTICE
OFFICE COORDINATOR: MEGAN MADRIGAL
ASPENSTORE.COM: CHRIS RUPP

To find the
Comic Shop
nearest you...

COMIC SHOP LOCATOR SERVICE
888-COMIC-BOOK
csls.diamondcomics.com
1-888-266-4226

CHAPTER

ZERO

HEAD GAMES

THE SUIT. THREE O'CLOCK.

I SAW. I'M ON HIM. A HIJACKER. NOT VERY ORIGINAL.

I GUESS THE CLASSICS NEVER GO OUT OF STYLE.

WE'LL TAKE HIM TOGETHER.

FORGET IT, I GOT THIS FOOL.

ERIKA, WAIT...

Crap.

BETTER DEACTIVATE WHATEVER'S INSIDE. HE MIGHT HAVE A REMOTE TRIGGER. AND BE CAREFUL.

I KNOW WHAT I'M DOING.

FAMOUS LAST WORDS.

OUTTA THE WAY! MOVE! LOOKOUT!

Screw this.

GIVE IT UP, LOSER.

WITHOUT YOUR BRIEFCASE, YOU COULDN'T HIJACK AN EXTRA BAG OF PEANUTS.

THAT'S WHAT YOU THINK. THE BRIEFCASE WAS JUST A DECOY.

I'M THE PACKAGE--

--LOSER.

NOT A BAD WAY FOR WANNABE ACTORS TO SPEND THEIR TIME, I GUESS.

DO YOU THINK THEY WOULD VOLUNTEER FOR THIS SIMULATION, IF THEY KNEW WHAT *WE* WERE CAPABLE OF?

PROBABLY NOT.

WOULD YOU HAVE SIGNED ON FOR THE PROGRAM, IF *YOU* KNEW WHAT WE'D BE CAPABLE OF?

GOOD POINT.

AIN'T NO BIG SURPRISE THOUGH. ALWAYS KNEW THE WORLD WAS SH*T. THE ONLY DIFFERENCE IS NOW WE GOT THE PROOF.

YEAH...

DAMN, *IGNORANCE* WAS BLISS.

"I DON'T SEE THEIR FACES,
BUT I KNOW THEIR SECRETS...
AND I *F***ING* HATE THAT."
—CONNOR

ASPEN COMICS

AND

J.T. KRUL

PRESENT

CREATED & WRITTEN BY_ **J.T. KRUL**

PENCILS BY_ **ALEX KONAT**

INKS BY_ **JON BOLERJACK**
& SALEEM CRAWFORD, RICHARD ZAJAC
(CHAPTER 0, 1)   (CHAPTER 2)

COLORS BY_ **JOHN STARR**

LETTERS BY_ **JOSH REED**

PROJECT COBALT DATA FILES:
WRITTEN BY_ **J.T. KRUL**
ARTWORK BY_ **LORI "CROSS" HANSON**
COLORS BY_ **SIYA OUM**

CHAPTER

ONE

AN INSIDE JOB

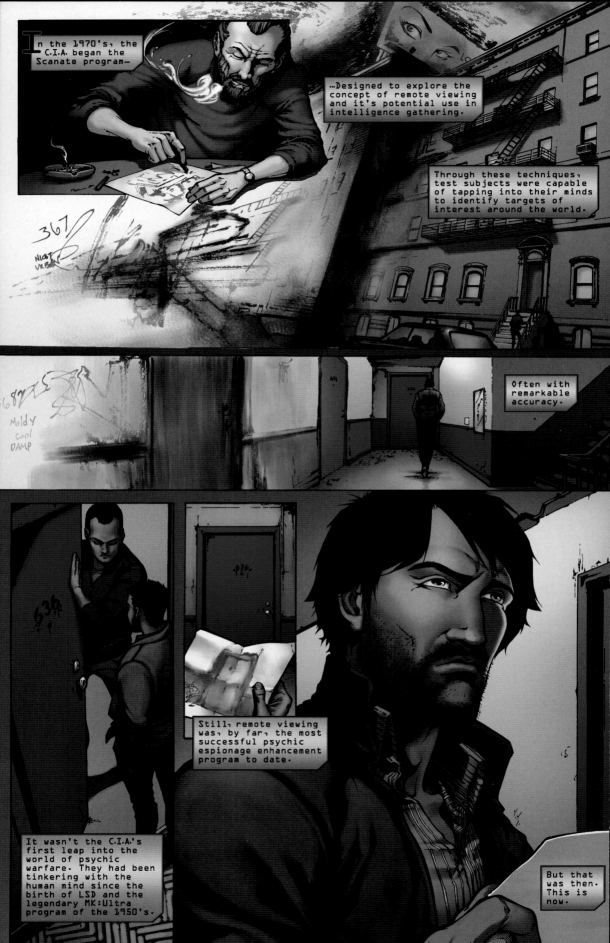

In the 1970's, the C.I.A. began the Scanate program...

...Designed to explore the concept of remote viewing and it's potential use in intelligence gathering.

Through these techniques, test subjects were capable of tapping into their minds to identify targets of interest around the world.

367

NIGHT VISION

687

Moldy Cool DAMP

Often with remarkable accuracy.

636

636

636

Still, remote viewing was, by far, the most successful psychic espionage enhancement program to date.

It wasn't the C.I.A.'s first leap into the world of psychic warfare. They had been tinkering with the human mind since the birth of LSD and the legendary MK:Ultra program of the 1950's.

But that was then. This is now.

I GOT'EM!

BLAM

DAMN.

ISAAC...?

I *SAID*, I GOT'EM!

WHAT'S THE STORY?

IT'S A FOOT RACE.

MY MONEY'S ON *ISAAC*. THAT BOY CAN *MOVE*.

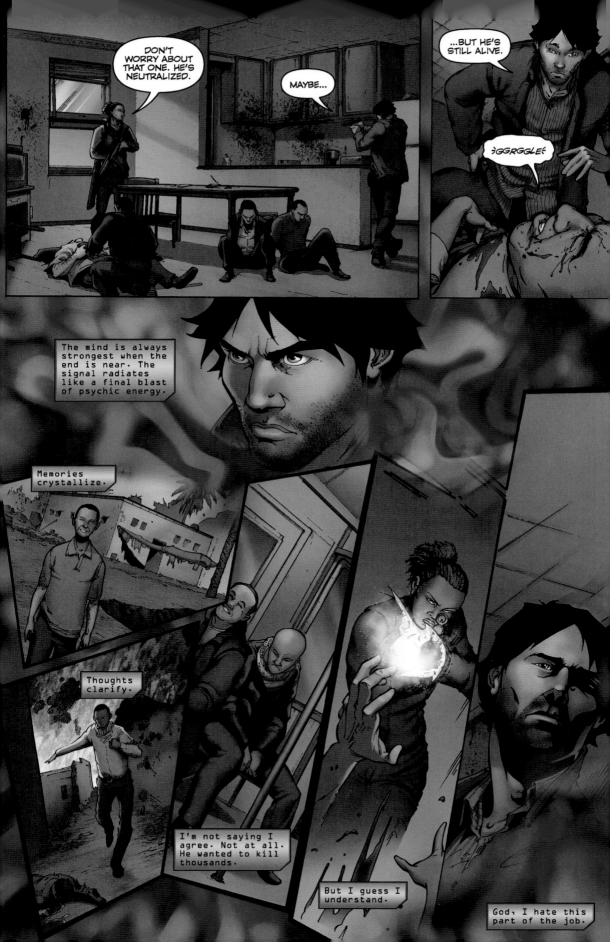

--IS BEING HAILED AS A *MAJOR* BREAKUP OF A *TERRORIST* THREAT.

ACCORDING TO *F.B.I.* OFFICIALS, FIVE SUSPECTS WERE IN THE PROCESS OF CONSTRUCTING SEVERAL EXPLOSIVE DEVICES WITH INTENT TO DETONATE THEM IN NEW YORK'S SUBWAY SYSTEM--

F.B.I. OFFICIALS-- *WHATEVER.*

LOOK AT THEM STRUTTING AROUND IN THEIR WINDBREAKERS. THEY DIDN'T DO A DAMN THING BUT PICK UP THE PHONE WHEN *WE* CALLED'EM.

THEY COULD HAVE AT LEAST INCLUDED ONE *MIDDLE EASTERNER* FROM THE BUREAU FOR THE *PHOTO-OP.*

IT LOOKS LIKE THE *ARYAN RACE* IS BRINGING IN THE *SONS OF ALLAH.*

POSERS. IT'S LIKE MY OLD ASSIGNMENT. WE DO THE DIRTY WORK-- GET THE JOB DONE-- AND SOMEONE ELSE TAKES ALL THE CREDIT.

I THOUGHT NAVY *SEALS* WEREN'T ABOUT THE GLORY?

STICK WITH YOUR *BOOK,* CONNOR. I WASN'T TALKING TO YOU.

THEN WHO *WERE* YOU TALKING TO?

I ASSUME HIS ANIMOSITY IS DIRECTED AT ME, ERIKA.

ISAAC, I HAD NO IDEA THE COVERT NATURE OF THIS PROGRAM WOULD UPSET YOUR GENTLE SENSIBILITIES.

NOW...

...I KNOW THIS EXPERIENCE HAS BEEN AN ORDEAL FOR ALL OF YOU-- PHYSICALLY AND MENTALLY. BUT THIS IS WHAT *PROJECT COBALT* IS ALL ABOUT. LAST NIGHT WAS OUR FIRST FIELD OPERATION, AND YOU DIDN'T DISAPPOINT. YOU SAVED COUNTLESS LIVES.

YET, YOU ALL LOOK LIKE A BUNCH OF *MOODY* BASTARDS.

NO?

HOW ABOUT THE FACT THAT I'M GIVING YOU ALL THE NIGHT OFF?

CONSIDER IT AN EVENING *FURLOUGH*. ENJOY SOME DOWN TIME. *CELEBRATE*.

WOULD IT HELP IF I TOLD YOU WE GOT A CALL FROM SECRETARY OF STATE HARPER?

HE CONVEYED THE *PRESIDENT'S* SINCEREST APPRECIATION FOR THE CIA'S EFFORTS.

BUT BE READY TO GO IN THE MORNING, BECAUSE WE'VE GOT A *LOT* MORE WORK AHEAD OF US.

LAST NIGHT WAS ONLY THE *BEGINNING*.

When the witching hour arrives...

...We must take our medicine or risk falling completely into the abyss.

None of us know exactly what's inside-- something McManus had the lab boys come up with.

What Dylan calls our magic pills-- we just call the Cobalt Blues.

A cerebral concoction of LSD, peyote, and every other hallucinogenic under the sun-- or over the rainbow, I suppose.

The funny thing is I avoided the whole drug scene altogether when I was younger. In college, I was strictly a keg man. I never took an interest in the heavy stuff.

Now look at me. The C.I.A. Changed my life. They made me a user. An addict.

A pill-popping, mind-reading freak.

Wonder if JFK knew that's what the government had in mind when he asked what we could do for our country?

what are the roots that clutch, what branches grow Out of this stony rubbish?

"Son of man, you cannot say, or guess, for you know only A heap of broken images, where the sun beats, and the dead tree gives no shelter, the cricket no relief...

"...and the dry stone no sound of water."

It's Eliot's The Wasteland. I don't know what it means, and that's the point. Focusing on memorized passages helps me keep the other minds at bay.

It provides a level of interference. That's my blocker.

But somehow things still worm their way through.

IT'S GOOD TO FINALLY MEET YOU, FACE-TO-FACE.

SO, WHERE IS IT?

RIGHT HERE.

TEN THOUSAND AS PROMISED.

SWEET. IT WAS A PIECE OF CAKE. GIVE ME A CHALLENGE NEXT TIME.

QUITE THE SETUP YOU GOT HERE.

UH... IF YOU DON'T MIND...? I'M KIND OF PROTECTIVE ABOUT MY SPACE.

WHATEVER, MAN. JUST CURIOUS.

SORRY.

WELL, WE'LL GET OUT OF YOUR WAY.

ENJOY YOUR MONEY.

MINDFIELD

PROJECT COBALT DATA FILES

PROJECT COBALT

SUBJECT: CONNOR
SCRIPT: J.T. KRUL
ARTWORK: LORI "CROSS" HANSON
COLORS: SIYA OUM

STOLEN MOMENTS

WE NEED TO UNDERSTAND THE *CHAIN* OF EVENTS THAT LED TO THE *ATTACK* ON THE MAN IN THE ALLEY.

CONNOR?

Billy Pilgrim… he became slightly unstuck in time…

"The formation flew backwards over a German city that was in flames.*

"The bombers opened their bomb bay doors, exerted a miraculous magnetism which shrunk the fires…

…gathered them into cylindrical steel containers, nd lifted the ontainers into he bellies of he planes.

"When the bombers got back to their base, the steel cylinders were taken from the racks and shipped back to the United States of America.

"Where factories were operating night and day, dismantling the cylinders, separating the dangerous contents into minerals.

"Touchingly, it was mainly women who did this work.

"The minerals were then shipped to specialists in remote areas.

"It was their business to put them into the ground, to hide them cleverly, so they would never hurt anybody again."

CONNOR?

*FROM KURT VONNEGUT'S SLAUGHTERHOUSE FIVE.

RANDALL WRIGHT. I'M THE FOUNDER AND CHAIRMAN OF *THE GLOBAL TRUST.*

FOR THE PAST FIFTEEN YEARS WE'VE CONDUCTED RESEARCH AND ANALYSIS ON A HOST OF VITAL *SOCIAL* AND *ECONOMIC* ISSUES-- FROM CRIME AND POVERTY TO EDUCATION AND THE ENVIRONMENT.

AND WHILE I HAVEN'T HAD THE PLEASURE OF WORKING *DIRECTLY* WITH THE *CIA* BEFORE, WE HAVE *CONSULTED* WITH THE FEDERAL GOVERNMENT ON ISSUES OF *NATIONAL SECURITY.*

THANKS FOR THE VERBAL *BROCHURE,* RANDALL, BUT WE'RE *NOT* HERE TO DISCUSS YOUR ROLE HERE AT THE GLOBAL TRUST.

WE'RE MORE INTERESTED IN YOUR *FORMATIVE* YEARS.

AS YOU CAN SEE, THE *AGE OF AQUARIUS* WAS A BUSY TIME FOR EVERYONE. WE KNOW ALL ABOUT YOUR PSYCHIC EXPERIMENTATION.

A REAL *JOHNNY APPLESEED* YOU WERE.

THAT... THAT WAS A *LIFETIME* AGO.

WELL-- FUNNY THING ABOUT THE *PAST.* IT'S *ALWAYS* THERE.

I'M CONFUSED. ARE YOU HERE TO *ARREST* ME?

ON THE CONTRARY. WE *NEED* YOU.

YEP. NAME'S *CONNOR*.

HE'S SHOWN *REMARKABLE* RESPONSE, BUT HE'S HAVING TROUBLE COPING WITH THE *PSYCHOTROPIC* COMPONENT.

CONSIDERING THE DOSAGE AND TYPES OF DRUGS YOU ARE PUTTING INTO HIS SYSTEM, I'M SURPRISED HE'S EVEN *COGNITIVE*.

LET'S BE *CLEAR*. ALL YOU NEED TO DO IS HELP HIM QUELL THE *DEMONS* AND GET HIS HEAD BACK ON STRAIGHT SO HE CAN FUNCTION.

YOU'RE *NOT* HIS THERAPIST. YOU GOT ME?

SURE. YOU DON'T WANT TO *FIX* HIS NOGGIN. JUST KEEP IT FROM *CRACKING*.

WELL-- CRACKING ANY *FURTHER*.

I'M A LITTLE IN THE *DARK* MYSELF-- NOT KNOWING THE EXACT NATURE OF YOUR TREATMENT'S *AGENDA.*

BUT SUCH VISIONS ARE RATHER *COMMONPLACE* WHEN *EXPLORING* PSYCHIC BOUNDARIES.

THEY ARE?

ABSOLUTELY, CONNOR.

YOUR TETHERS OF *CONNECTIVITY* ARE THE LIFELINES TO *NIRVANA* AND COMPLETE *ENLIGHTENMENT,* BUT THEY CAN ALSO REVEAL THE OTHER SIDE OF THE *SPECTRUM--* TOTAL *OBLIVION.*

YOU WILL INEVITABLY *DISCOVER* BOTH WHEN *PEELING* AWAY THE LAYERS OF THE HUMAN MIND.

YEAH. WELL, THERE WAS DEFINITELY *PEELING.*

You can see it in Dylan. Whenever he's called upon to RV* an object.

*REMOTE VIEW.

He sits at his chair, turns down the lights, and simply flips a switch.

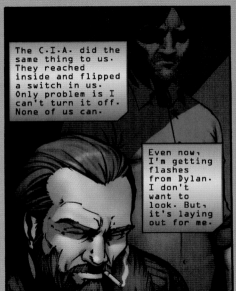

The C.I.A. did the same thing to us. They reached inside and flipped a switch in us. Only problem is I can't turn it off. None of us can.

Even now, I'm getting flashes from Dylan. I don't want to look. But, it's laying out for me.

Like a train wreck.

I can't help but see.

What he had.

What he lost.

And the empty husk that remains.

<CHICAGO, ILLINOIS.>>

SO, HOW WE LOOKING?

WORKING ON IT.

YOU GOT ON FIVE STOPS AGO. YOU CAN'T READ HIM YET?

SHOULD HAVE STAYED ON THE SIDELINES.

STOP BUGGING ME.

OKAY, LADIES AND GENTLEMEN-- TIME TO SHOW ME WHAT YOU GOT.

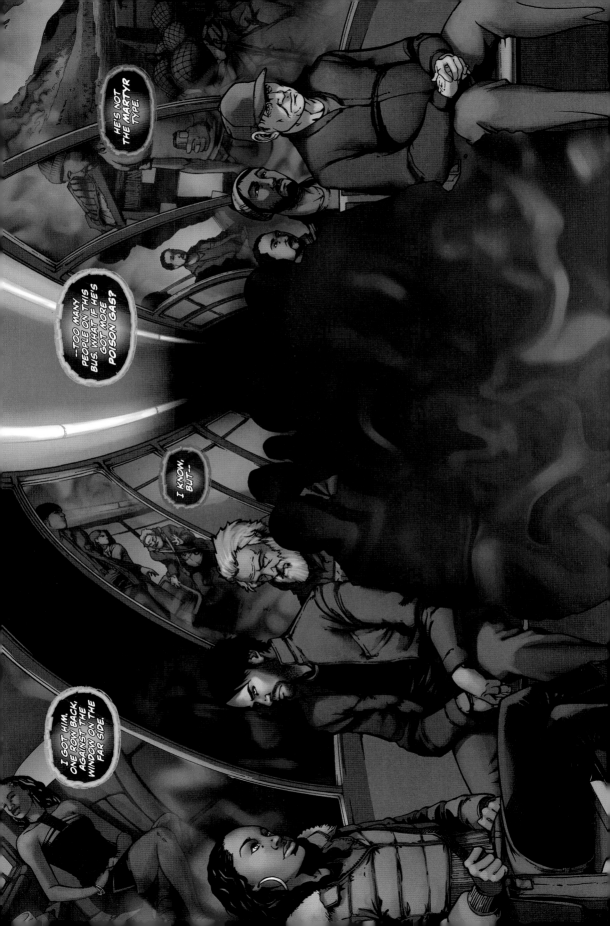

I'M TAKIN' HIM!

NO! WAIT!

HE'S DOWN.

THAT'S GREAT, ISAAC...

STAY AWAY... I'LL SPLATTER HER BRAINS ALL OVER THE BUS!

...HOW ABOUT THE OTHER ONE?

HELP... ME...

ERIKA!

I HEAR YOU.

AND I *SEE* YOU.

AiiIEEEE!

WHAT'S THE MATTER, SON? WEREN'T YOU BOYS READY TO *DIE* FOR YOUR CAUSE?

"DO NOT *IGNORE* THAT RINGING IN YOUR EAR-- *HEAR* US.

"DO NOT *FIGHT* THAT GNAWING SENSATION IN YOUR STOMACH-- *FEEL* US.

"DO NOT *SHUT* YOUR MIND OFF FROM THE POSSIBILITIES-- *KNOW* US."

MINDFIELD

PROJECT COBALT DATA FILES

PROJECT COBALT

SUBJECT: ERIKA
SCRIPT: J.T. KRUL
ARTWORK: LORI "CROSS" HANSON
COLORS: SIYA OUM

CHAPTER

THREE

DIGGING DEEP

SO... WHAT'S THE GOOD WORD, MALCOLM?

YOU KNOW THE SAYING, LUCIEN. A *MIND* IS A TERRIBLE THING TO *WASTE.*

PRESENT COMPANY *EXCLUDED.*

BUT HE DID OFFER US ONE USEFUL *NUGGET.*

AH, *EXCELLENT.* YOU NEVER DISAPPOINT.

I THINK WE ARE *DONE* WITH HIM, *STAN.*

PUT HIM WITH THE OTHERS OUT BACK.

YOU GOT IT.

AND *SOON--* I DON'T WANT HIM *SOILING* HIMSELF IN MY *HOUSE.*

"THE BIGGEST *MISNOMER* IS THAT THE *JOURNEY* IS ABOUT *FOCUS*-- ABOUT FINDING ONE'S *SELF.*

"WHEN THE EXACT *OPPOSITE* IS *TRUE.* OUR SENSE OF SELF, OUR *IDENTITY*-- IT'S THE *DISTRACTION.*

"WE *CRIPPLE* OUR *MINDS* WITH THE *MEMORIES* OF PAST *SINS;* THE GLOW OF IMAGINED *PLEASURE,* AND THE NAGGING *ITCH* OF PREVIOUS *HUMILIATIONS.*

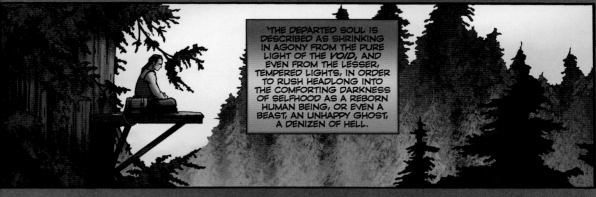

"THESE ARE THE *EMOTIONS*-- FEAR, HATRED, LUST-- THAT *ECLIPSE* THE VIEW OF THE *LIGHT.*

'THE DEPARTED SOUL IS DESCRIBED AS SHRINKING IN AGONY FROM THE PURE LIGHT OF THE *VOID,* AND EVEN FROM THE LESSER, TEMPERED LIGHTS, IN ORDER TO RUSH HEADLONG INTO THE COMFORTING DARKNESS OF SELFHOOD AS A REBORN HUMAN BEING, OR EVEN A BEAST, AN UNHAPPY GHOST, A DENIZEN OF HELL.

'ANYTHING RATHER THAN THE BURNING BRIGHTNESS OF UNMITIGATED REALITY-- ANYTHING!'"*

*FROM THE DOORS OF PERCEPTION, ALDOUS HUXLEY.

THE *VOID*, HUH? SOUNDS *PEACHY*.

I THOUGHT YOU WERE SUPPOSED TO MAKE ME FEEL *BETTER* ABOUT THESE *HEAD* GAMES.

I'M TRYING TO *EXPLAIN* THAT WHAT YOU ARE *EXPERIENCING* IS NOT SO AGAINST OUR *PSYCHIC MAKEUP*.

HUXLEY SAID THAT EVERYONE IS CAPABLE OF KNOWING *EVERYTHING* THAT *WAS* AND *IS* CURRENTLY HAPPENING THROUGHOUT THE *UNIVERSE*--

--A TRUE *COLLECTIVE UNCONSCIOUS* PERHAPS.

IT'S OUR *BRAIN*, OUR PRAGMATIC, NERVOUS SYSTEM CONTROLLING BRAIN THAT CUTS US OFF FROM THAT *CONNECTION*-- *ISOLATING* ONLY TO THAT WHICH IS DEEMED *PRACTICAL* AND *USEFUL*.

DON'T START REFERRING TO MY *CONDITION* AS A *GIFT*.

I WON'T. BUT THE ABILITY YOU POSSESS, THE CONNECTIONS YOU CAN MAKE-- ONE COULD ARGUE THAT THEY MAKE YOU *MORE HUMAN* THAN *HUMAN*.

THEN BEING HUMAN IS ALL ABOUT *DEPRESSION, ANXIETY, FEAR,* AND *RAGE*-- BECAUSE THAT'S WHAT THESE CONNECTIONS ARE ALL ABOUT.

EXCEPT FOR THOSE WHO KNOW HOW TO *CLOSE* THEIR *MINDS* OFF-- LIKE ERIKA AND ISAAC AND MCMANUS...

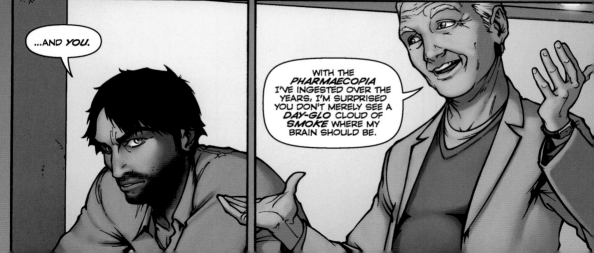

...AND *YOU*.

WITH THE *PHARMAECOPIA* I'VE INGESTED OVER THE YEARS, I'M SURPRISED YOU DON'T MERELY SEE A *DAY-GLO* CLOUD OF *SMOKE* WHERE MY BRAIN SHOULD BE.

NAME'S **WEBSTER BLAKE**.

A MID-LEVEL **PROGRAMMER** WHO DID CONTRACT WORK FOR THE **D.O.D.**

HIS WAS ONE OF THE NAMES LIFTED FROM THE HACKER JOB. AND NOW, HE'S GONE **MISSING**.

WHAT **KIND** OF **WORK** DID HE DO FOR THE DEPARTMENT?

ON PAPER, IT WAS PURELY ADMINISTRATIVE.

TOOK SOME **CLEARANCE**, BUT I FOUND OUT HE WAS ONE OF THE PROGRAMMERS TASKED WITH REDESIGNING THE **PASS CODE PROTOCOL** FOR THE LATEST U.S. **NUCLEAR WARHEAD** STOCKPILE.

GREAT.

YOU'RE SAYING THIS GUY-- THE ONE KIDNAPPED--HE KNOWS THE CODES TO **DETONATE** A **WARHEAD?**

NOT EXACTLY.

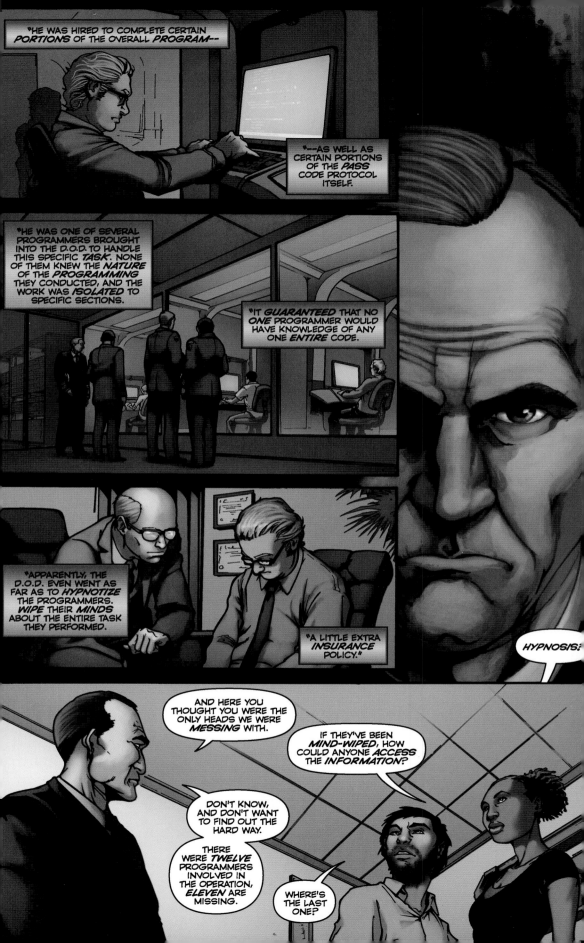

FREUD SAID IT BEST.

"HOMO HOMINI LUPUS.

"MEN ARE *NOT* GENTLE *CREATURES* WHO WANT TO BE *LOVED*, AND WHO AT THE MOST CAN *DEFEND* THEMSELVES IF THEY ARE *ATTACKED*.

"THEY ARE, ON THE CONTRARY, CREATURES AMONG WHOSE INSTINCTUAL ENDOWMENTS IS TO BE RECKONED A POWERFUL SHARE OF *AGGRESSIVENESS*.

"...TO *HUMILIATE* HIM; TO CAUSE HIM *PAIN*, TO *TORTURE* AND *KILL* HIM.

"HOMO HOMINI LUPUS.

"AS A RESULT, THEIR *NEIGHBOUR* IS FOR THEM NOT ONLY A POTENTIAL *HELPER* OR *SEXUAL OBJECT*, BUT ALSO SOMEONE WHO *TEMPTS* THEM TO *SATISFY* THEIR AGGRESSIVENESS ON HIM.

"MAN IS *WOLF* TO MAN."

"TO *EXPLOIT* HIS CAPACITY FOR WORK WITHOUT *COMPENSATION*; TO *USE* HIM SEXUALLY WITHOUT HIS CONSENT; TO *SEIZE* HIS POSSESSIONS...

MINDFIELD

PROJECT COBALT DATA FILES

PROJECT COBALT

SUBJECT: ISAAC
SCRIPT: J.T. KRUL
ARTWORK: LORI "CROSS" HANSON
COLORS: SIYA OUM

THE *TALIBAN* THINK WE'RE *WEAK*-- THAT WE AREN'T *MOTIVATED* IN THIS FIGHT-- THAT WE LACK *COMMITMENT.*

THEY THINK WE'RE LIKE THE *RUSSIANS.* THEY'RE *WRONG.*

AND IT'S NOT THE ONLY *MISTAKE* THEY MAKE.

THUK

THUK
THUK
THUK

NIGHTS LIKE TONIGHT HAVE A WAY OF DIGGING THEIR WAY INTO MY MEMORY.

I'LL EASILY PUT THE MILES AND THE MONTHS BETWEEN US, BUT EVERYTHING ELSE-- THAT'LL STICK RIGHT WITH ME.

FOREVER.

CHAPTER

FOUR

BAD TRIP DOWN MEMORY LANE

Because running through other people's memories is a lot like being inside their nightmares.

You're scared. You don't know why, but you're scared anyway.

THAT'S IT THEN.

THAT'S HOW YOU'RE ABLE TO GET AT THE CODES BURIED IN THESE PROGRAMMERS' HEADS.

GETTING PRETTY CROWDED IN HERE.

WHAT'S THE MATTER? THOUGHT YOU WERE THE ONLY MEMBERS IN THE CLUB?

JUST A MATTER OF SCRAMBLING THE EGGS.

YOU KNOW ALL ABOUT THAT I BET-- FROM PERSONAL EXPERIENCE.

UHNNGH!

LET HER GO!

GUESS YOU'RE NOT USED TO PHYSICAL CONFRONTATION IN HERE.

YOU GOT ME THERE.

BUT NOTHING ABOUT THIS REALM IS PHYSICAL. RIGHT, IAN?

WHAT... IS... HE... DOING?

MINDFIELD

PROJECT COBALT DATA FILES

PROJECT COBALT

SUBJECT: KASEEM
SCRIPT: J.T. KRUL
ARTWORK: LORI "CROSS" HANSON
COLORS: SIYA OUM

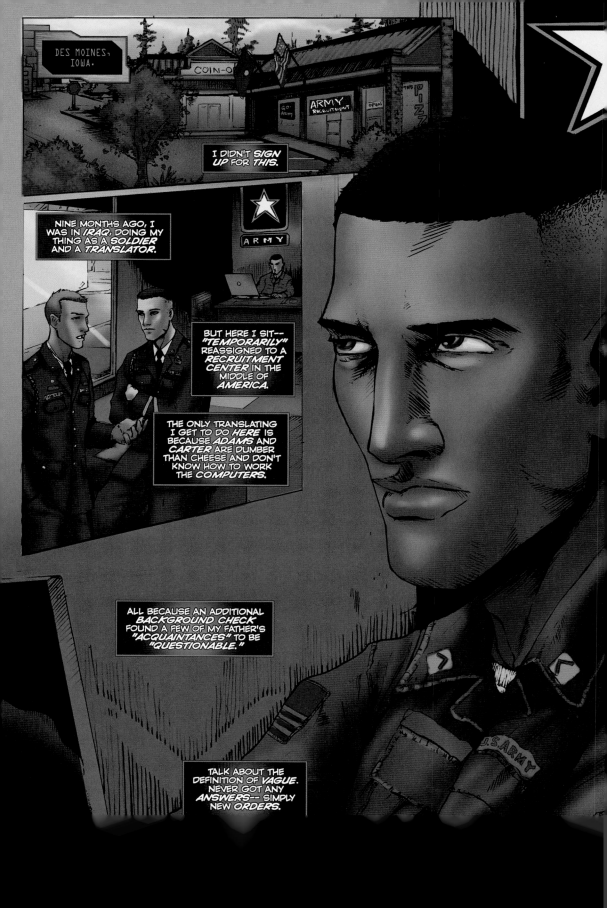

DES MOINES, IOWA.

I DIDN'T *SIGN UP* FOR *THIS.*

NINE MONTHS AGO, I WAS IN *IRAQ,* DOING MY THING AS A *SOLDIER* AND A *TRANSLATOR.*

BUT HERE I SIT-- *"TEMPORARILY"* REASSIGNED TO A *RECRUITMENT CENTER* IN THE MIDDLE OF *AMERICA.*

THE ONLY TRANSLATING I GET TO DO *HERE* IS BECAUSE *ADAMS* AND *CARTER* ARE DUMBER THAN CHEESE AND DON'T KNOW HOW TO WORK THE *COMPUTERS.*

ALL BECAUSE AN ADDITIONAL *BACKGROUND CHECK* FOUND A FEW OF MY FATHER'S *"ACQUAINTANCES"* TO BE *"QUESTIONABLE."*

TALK ABOUT THE DEFINITION OF *VAGUE.* NEVER GOT ANY *ANSWERS*-- SIMPLY NEW *ORDERS.*

CHAPTER

FIVE

CAUSE AND EFFECT

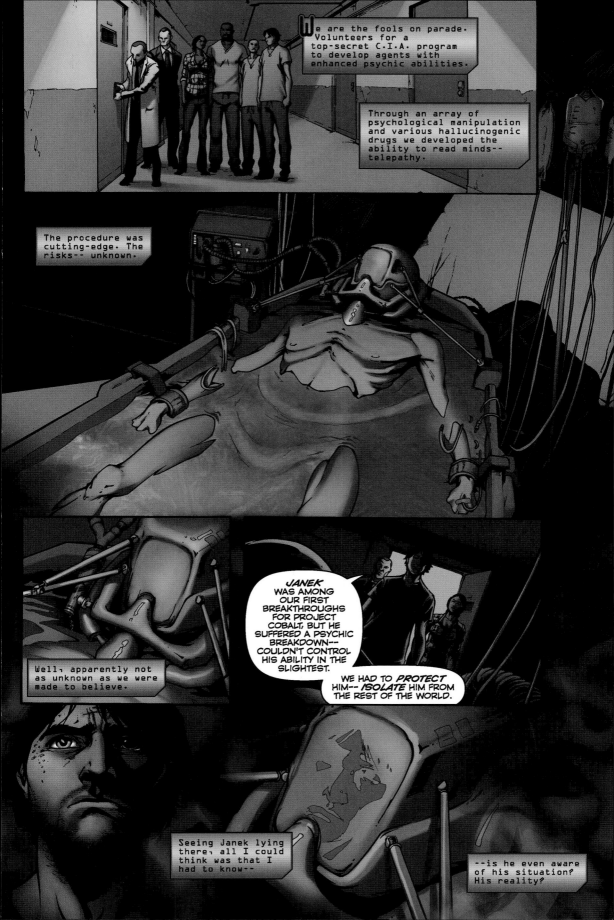

We are the fools on parade. Volunteers for a top-secret C.I.A. program to develop agents with enhanced psychic abilities.

Through an array of psychological manipulation and various hallucinogenic drugs we developed the ability to read minds-- telepathy.

The procedure was cutting-edge. The risks-- unknown.

Well, apparently not as unknown as we were made to believe.

JANEK WAS AMONG OUR FIRST BREAKTHROUGHS FOR PROJECT COBALT, BUT HE SUFFERED A PSYCHIC BREAKDOWN-- COULDN'T CONTROL HIS ABILITY IN THE SLIGHTEST.

WE HAD TO PROTECT HIM-- ISOLATE HIM FROM THE REST OF THE WORLD.

Seeing Janek lying there, all I could think was that I had to know--

--is he even aware of his situation? His reality?

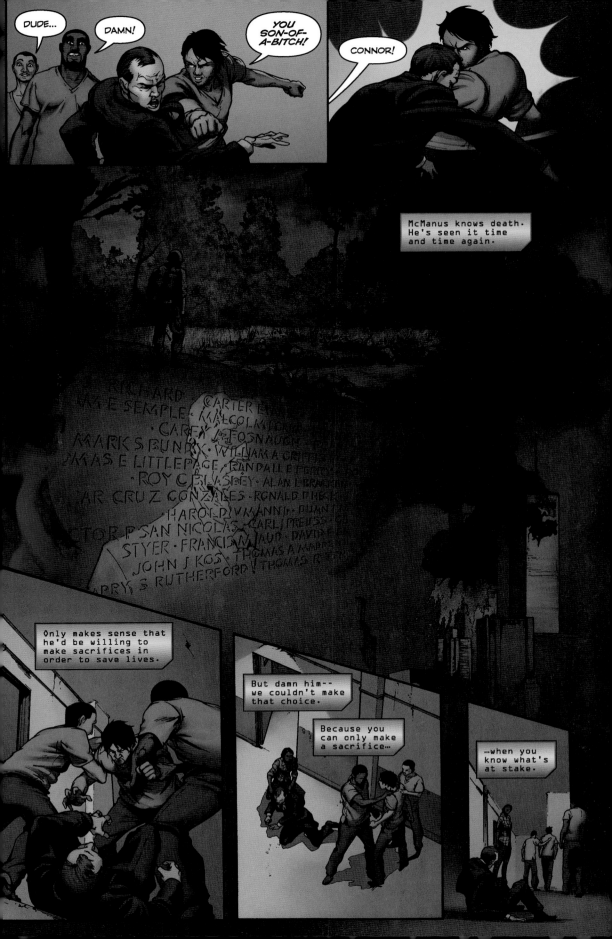

WHAT ABOUT YOU?

AM I THE ONLY ONE WHO'S *PISSED* ABOUT THIS?

DON'T BE SO *DRAMATIC*. IT SUCKS. BUT NOT MUCH WE CAN DO ABOUT IT. BESIDES, IT *DOESN'T* CHANGE ANYTHING.

IT WAS THE ONLY WAY I COULD ACTUALLY DO SOMETHING. AFTER 9/11 MY SKIN TONE MADE ME *UNDESIRABLE* FOR MOST EVERYTHING.

DOESN'T CHANGE ANYTHING?!?

IT CHANGES *EVERYTHING!*

WE KNEW GOING IN-- THIS PROGRAM WAS GOING TO BE... *MURKY* AT BEST. IT'S THE DEFINITION OF *TOP-SECRET*.

WE STILL GOT A *JOB* TO DO AND THE *MEANS* TO DO IT.

KASEEM, DO YOU UNDERSTAND WHAT THE HELL SHE IS TALKING ABOUT?

I DO. AT THE END OF THE DAY, IT'S STILL ABOUT STOPPING THE *BAD* GUYS.

YEAH? WELL-- THANKS TO MCMANUS AND HIS PROGRAM-- *ALL I* SEE IS THE *BAD.* IN *EVERYONE.*

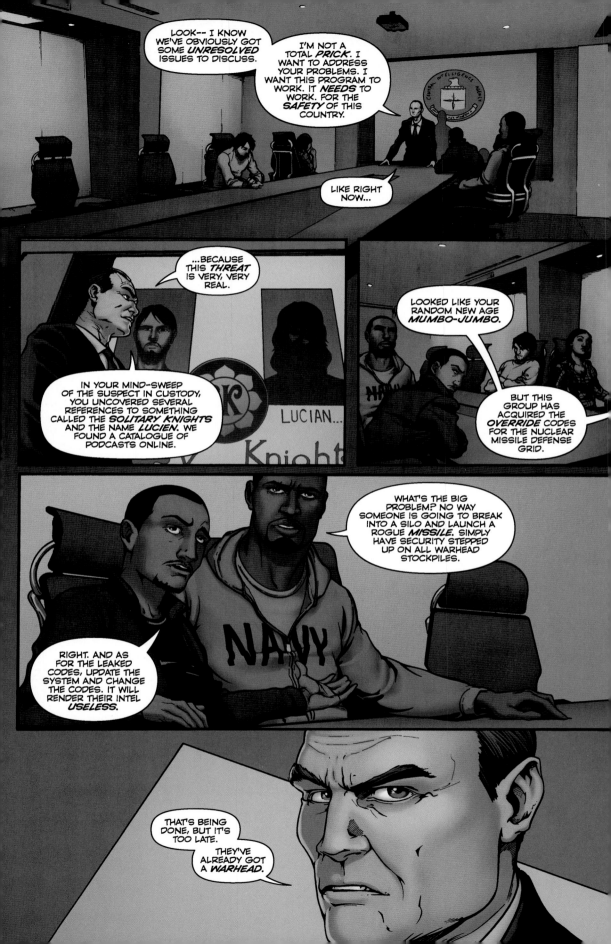

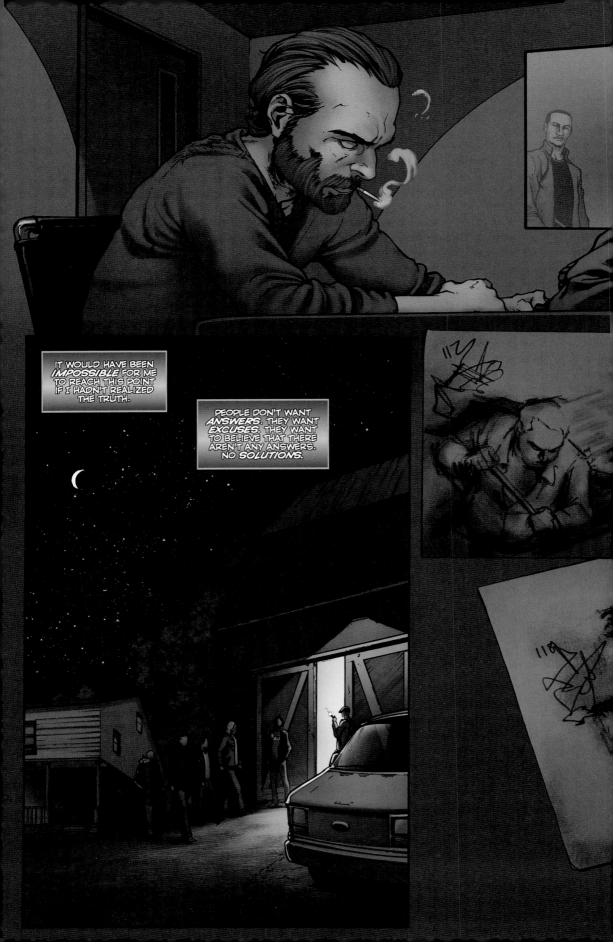

IT WOULD HAVE BEEN *IMPOSSIBLE* FOR ME TO REACH THIS POINT IF I HADN'T REALIZED THE TRUTH.

PEOPLE DON'T WANT *ANSWERS*. THEY WANT *EXCUSES*. THEY WANT TO BELIEVE THAT THERE AREN'T ANY ANSWERS. NO *SOLUTIONS*.

PPFFT

PPFFT

The soldiers have been trained to detect and confront the enemies as they come across them. It's their way.

We got our own way. Find the holes-- the place without any mental signatures. That way, we know our coast is clear.

MY GOD...

WHAT'S WRONG?

MINDFIELD

PROJECT COBALT DATA FILES

PROJECT COBALT

SUBJECT: McMANUS
SCRIPT: J.T. KRUL
ARTWORK: LORI "CROSS" HANSON
COLORS: SIYA OUM

CHAPTER

SIX

GAME CHANGER

AHHHHH!

MORNING, FELLAS!

WE ALL KNOW YOU GOT SOME SENSITIVE *CARGO* BACK THERE, SO BE *COOL.* THE ROAD TRIP IS *OVER.*

ALL THEY NEED TO DO IS PUSH A BUTTON, AND THIS THING BLOWS.
LET'S SEE HOW YOU LIKE IT. IT MAY ONLY BE IN YOUR MIND--
--BUT IT HURTS A HELL OF A LOT WORSE.
Can't stop him.
He's too strong.
Gotta find an angle. Do something unexpected.
If Malcolm is focusing his energy here, maybe he's vulnerable--

--at home.

Not exactly what I pictured inside the mind of a raging psychopath.

SHUT UP, *IAN.*

WHAT'S THAT SUPPOSED TO MEAN?

HURRY UP, MALCOLM. YOU RUN LIKE A *GIRL.*

PROBABLY EXACTLY WHAT YOU THINK, *CHLOE.*

HEY, *MALCOLM.*

DO I KNOW YOU?

SORT OF. YOU *WILL.*

I KNOW.

SORRY, *KID.*

HUH? I *DON'T* UNDERSTAND.

ERIKA? YOU OKAY?
YEAH, I'M FINE. THANKS.
WHERE DID THEY GO?
I THINK WE'RE *ALONE* NOW IN HERE.
DID YOU *KILL* THEM?
I DON'T KNOW.
WHAT ABOUT *LUCIEN?*
WE'RE RUNNING *OUT* OF TIME!
I *KNOW.*
YOU CAN'T *SAVE* THIS WORLD! YOU CAN'T STOP THE *FUTURE!*
THIS *CIVILIZATION* IS BANKRUPT-- MORALLY, EMOTIONALLY, FINANCIALLY.
THE ONLY WAY TO SAVE IT IS TO *DESTROY* IT AND REBUILD FROM *SCRATCH.*
You go, dude. Keep talking.
Erika's right. We're running out of time. Gotta stop this guy from pushing his button-- from detonating.
I know what I can do. But don't know if I can handle it.
Then again-- like everything else about this ability...

…I never really had a choice, did I?
Just like he never had a chance.
NOOO!
Once I got inside his head…

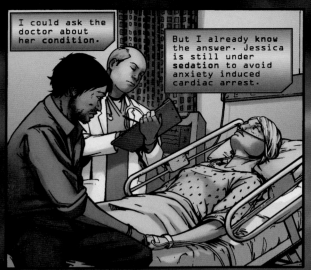

I could ask the doctor about her condition.

But I already know the answer. Jessica is still under sedation to avoid anxiety induced cardiac arrest.

Can't say I'd be any better if I saw the person I love gunned down in front of me, then had my mind essentially raped by a couple of psychic psychos.

I got a taste of what she was going through when I was trying to protect her from them.

The loss. The despair.

But just then, I wasn't seeing it--

THE END?

MINDFIELD

PROJECT COBALT DATA FILES

PROJECT COBALT

SUBJECT: RANDALL WRIGHT
SCRIPT: J.T. KRUL
ARTWORK: LORI "CROSS" HANSON
COLORS: SIYA OUM

"IN A SOCIETY FILLED
WITH TALK OF FEAR,
ENMITY, LUST, GREED,
KILLING, VIOLENCE,
RAGE, HATRED, DISEASE,
FAMINE, AND TERROR...

...WATCH WHAT YOU
THINK."

—CONNOR

COVER GALLERY

DIRECT EDITION COVER A TO
MINDFIELD #0
BY
ALEX KONAT | MARK ROSLAN | PETER STEIGERWALD

DIRECT EDITION COVER B TO
MINDFIELD #0
BY
PHIL NOTO

RETAILER INCENTIVE EXCLUSIVE EDITION COVER C TO
MINDFIELD #0
BY
JOE BENITEZ | MARK ROSLAN | PETER STEIGERWALD

DIRECT EDITION COVER A TO
MINDFIELD #1
BY
ALEX KONAT | MARK ROSLAN | PETER STEIGERWALD

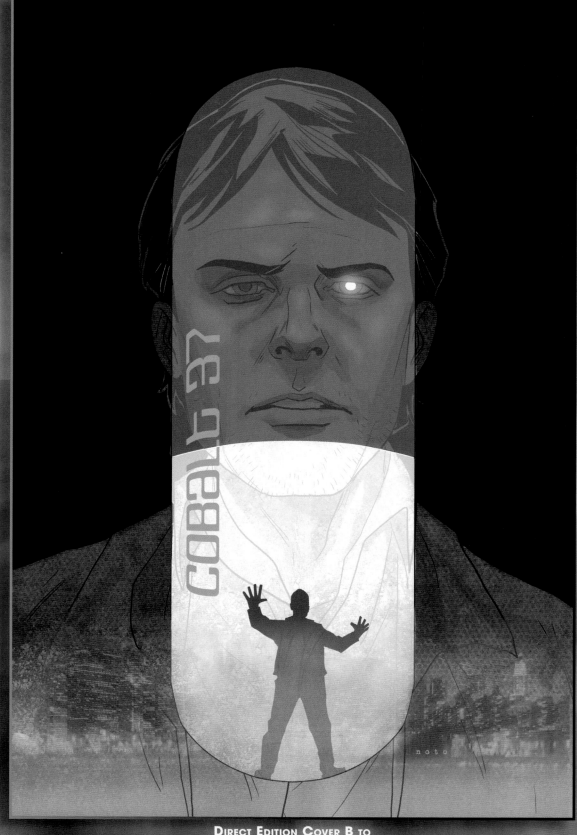

DIRECT EDITION COVER B TO
MINDFIELD #1
BY
PHIL NOTO

RETAILER INCENTIVE EXCLUSIVE EDITION COVER C TO
MINDFIELD #1
BY
JOE BENITEZ | MARK ROSLAN | PETER STEIGERWALD

DIRECT EDITION COVER A TO
MINDFIELD #2
BY
ALEX KONAT | MARK ROSLAN | JOHN STARR

Direct Edition Cover B to
MINDFIELD #2
BY
Phil NOTO

RETAILER "PSYCHEDELIC" INCENTIVE EDITION COVER C TO
MINDFIELD #2
BY
ALEX **KONAT** | MARK **ROSLAN** | PETER **STEIGERWALD**

SAN DIEGO COMIC-CON EXCLUSIVE EDITION LIMITED TO 250 COVER D TO
MINDFIELD #2
BY
ALEX KONAT | MARK ROSLAN

DIRECT EDITION COVER A TO
MINDFIELD #3
BY
Alex **KONAT** | Mark **ROSLAN** | John **STARR**

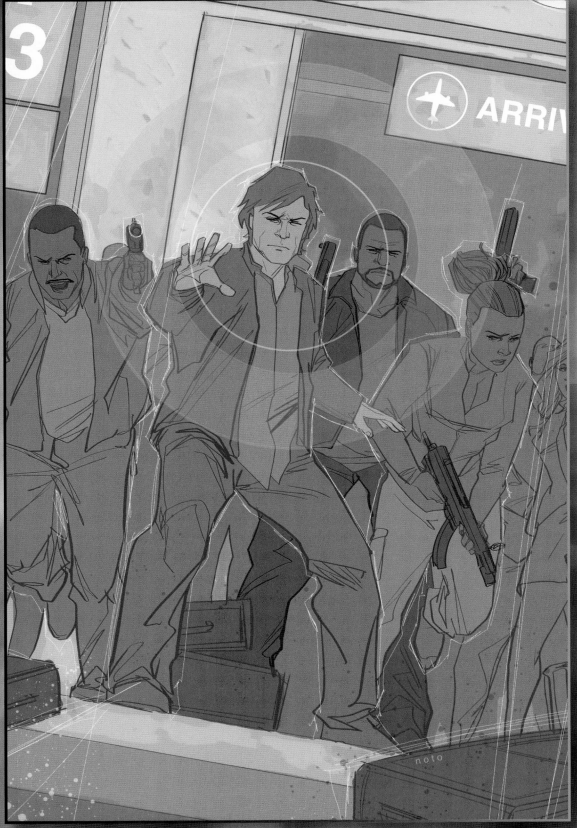

DIRECT EDITION COVER B TO
MINDFIELD #3
BY
PHIL NOTO

RETAILER "PSYCHEDELIC" INCENTIVE EDITION COVER C TO
MINDFIELD #3
BY
ALEX **KONAT** | MARK **ROSLAN** | PETER **STEIGERWALD**

DIRECT EDITION COVER A TO
MINDFIELD #4
BY
ALEX **KONAT** | MARK **ROSLAN** | JOHN **STARR**

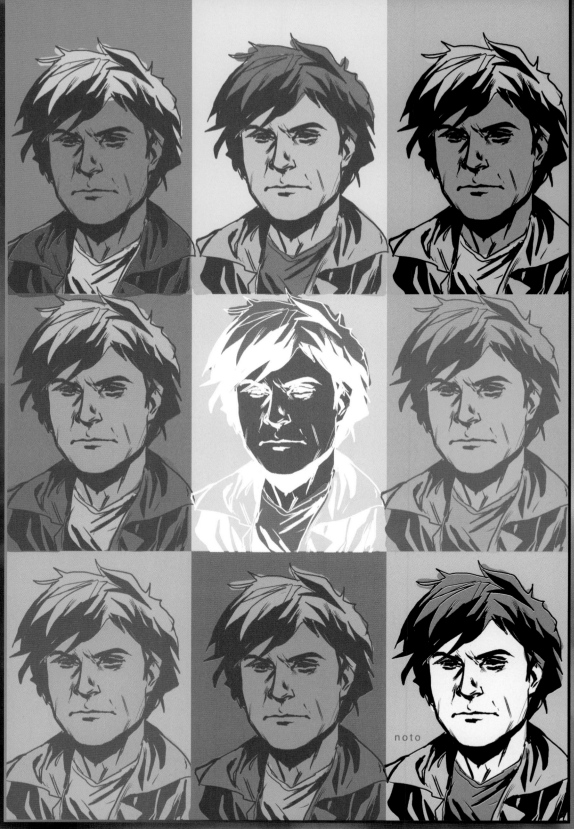

DIRECT EDITION COVER B TO
MINDFIELD #4
BY

PHIL NOTO

DIRECT EDITION COVER C TO
MINDFIELD #4
BY
ALEX SANCHEZ | MARK ROSLAN | JOHN STARR

DIRECT EDITION COVER D TO
MINDFIELD #4
BY
MICAH GUNNELL | PETER STEIGERWALD

RETAILER "PSYCHEDELIC" INCENTIVE EDITION COVER E TO
MINDFIELD #4
BY
ALEX **KONAT** | MARK **ROSLAN** | PETER **STEIGERWALD**

DIRECT EDITION COVER A TO
MINDFIELD #5
BY
ALEX **KONAT** | MARK **ROSLAN** | JOHN **STARR**

DIRECT EDITION COVER B to
MINDFIELD #5
BY
PHIL NOTO

DIRECT EDITION COVER A TO
MINDFIELD #6
BY
ALEX **KONAT** | MARK **ROSLAN** | JOHN **STARR**